THE BEST OF
SCENES FROM
FOOTBALL HISTORY

GW00759008

by Dave Robinson

WSC Books Ltd
17a Perseverance Works, 38 Kingsland Road, London E2 8DD
www.wsc.co.uk
info@wsc.co.uk

© WSC Books Ltd 2008
By Dave Robinson

ISBN 978-0-9561011-0-5

Printed in the UK by the MPG Books Group

Introduction

Having mastered the art of getting in the way of the skilful players during schoolyard kickabouts, I once nurtured dreams of "getting in the way" professionally. I would become a national treasure like Nobby Stiles – all I needed was an innocently clumsy demeanour and bad teeth (I was nearly there on both counts by the time I was 12). Desperate England managers would install me in midfield to obstruct the likes of Michel Platini and Johan Cruyff, and my illustrious international career would culminate in a deft bodycheck on Diego Maradona as he bore down on Peter Shilton in 1986. History might have been so different.

Which brings us to Scenes From Football History, an elastic "What if…?" premise that has been stretched to absurdity and beyond; though since we live in an age when those who control the domestic game and how we view it seem to have expunged anything that happened before the Premier League, I think my version of football's development may be just as valid.

The first Scene appeared as a cartoon in the *WSC* book *Offside*, published in 1989: a dubious effort featuring Adolf Hitler putting it about during a game in no-man's land in the First World War. The series Scenes From Football History began in *WSC* shortly afterwards with No 1, Scott of the Antarctic, and the rest is anachronistic, bastardised, controvertible history. It's a Marmite proposition – you either get it or you don't – but the idea has always offered up more potential for humour than football itself, wherein there are only three jokes, or four if you count Mark Lawrenson.

Dave Robinson, November 2008

Rations low. I have decided to lift our spirits with a spot of football. Should we meet Amundsen I shall challenge him to a game of ~~five~~ three a side.

The away fixture with Moscow Dynamo has taken its toll of the travelling support.

Moses has done an excellent job of drying out the pitch.

In an effort to achieve peak fitness this season Alf had given up the opium for good.

Mid-March: results still poor but the board were right behind Caesar.

Something told Higginbotham that he should have accepted that invitation to join the local masonic lodge after all...

Catering at the Galilee Cup Final was plentiful though somewhat limited in choice.

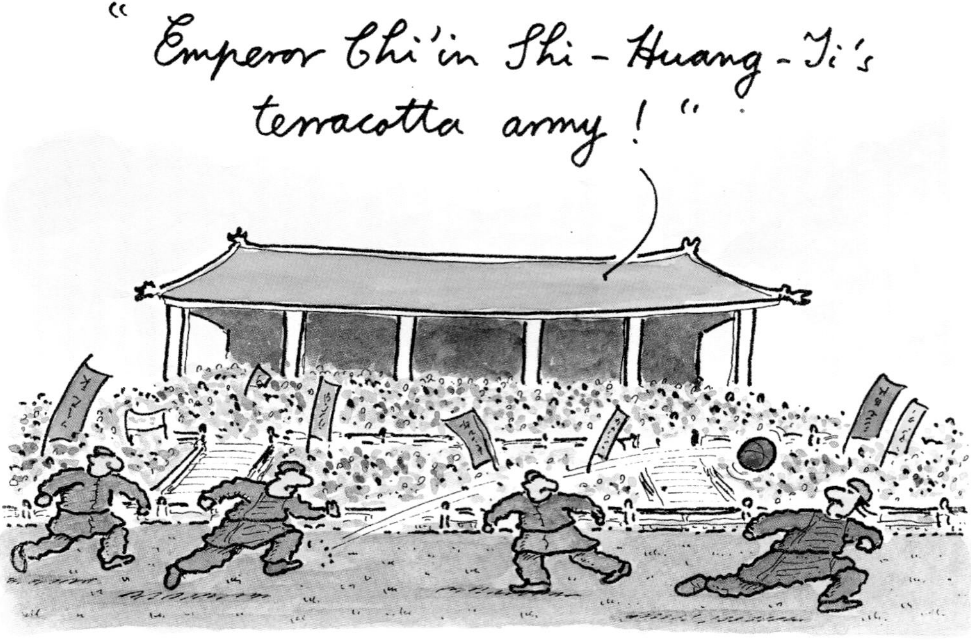
"Emperor Chi'in Shi-Huang-Ti's terracotta army!"

The new Transylvanian goalkeeper would only turn up for evening kick-offs.

The Montgolfier brothers had brought those stupid balloons to the game again.

Neville Chamberlain shows off the Cup Final tickets that he's bought from Herr Hitler.

Mao's long march ends ... in disappointment.

Lawrence insisted that the ball had gone over the camel and therefore was not a goal.

Life was tough at the foot of the Bolivian second division but the board were right behind the manager...well, in front of him actually.

Up for the cup, Bon Accord take the field determined to give Arbroath a bloody nose.

Sherpa Tensing has sliced his penalty 5000 feet down the South face. I shall jolly well make him go and get it!

... Jerusalem three, Damascus nil; Sodom versus Gomorrah — match postponed.

Alcock insisted that he could keep a ball up over a hundred times. Foolishly Brown bet him that he couldn't.

Isaac Newton explains that it had not been retaliation but rather an equal and opposite reaction.

Something needed to be done about limiting the number of players; picking a man of the match was proving almost impossible.

WILLIAM DE CANTONA PUTS KING HAROLDE OUT OF THE GAME FOR GOODE.

I don't know why we're even setting off, it's going to be rained off anyway.

Nostradamus fills in his fixed odds coupon ... more confidently than most.

We began to suspect that the coach driver didn't actually know where Port Vale was.

It was a pitch invasion by the transfer fee they'd received for their centre forward.

Dick Turpin had had enough; these football specials were more trouble than they were worth.

Groundsman Wilkins was not overly impressed with Mr. Stephenson's new steam mower.

It was Mr. Colombus the Littlewoods agent with next week's coupon.

All things considered, he'd have preferred a stiff fine and some community service.

It was Torquemada and the F.A. inquiry!

It was straightforward enough: if the manager floated he was sacked, and if he drowned then he had the full backing of the board.

Whatever was in his half-time cuppa, Dr. Jekyll was a different player in the second half.

Dr. Frankenstein had some peculiar ideas on how to treat a groin strain.

Seriously unhappy Greeks set off to get their ball back from the Trojans.

Smedley showed off his new shinpads.

Gutenberg produces the first match programme.
Something of a challenge for the programme sellers.

It was the tomb of one of ancient Egypt's less successful managers.

Unfortunately the dilapidated Druids' stadium is just not up to league standard.

The fourth official indicated that numbers had yet to be invented.

Prisoners of Stalag 19 sneak out to play their cup tie against Stalag 17. Winners at home to Colditz in the next round.

The Inca groundsman had been smoking the funny tobacco again.

The infallibility of His Holiness the referee is called into question during the Vatican Cup final.

The Japanese half-time tea ceremony delays kick-off for the second half.

Play is held up during a Queensland Cup match whilst the 'flying physio' is called on.

The 1666 cup final is abandoned as a hot dog stand overheats and sets London alight.

At last, thought Robinson Crusoe, someone
to go in goal.

The pygmies' cunning ploy of leaving the grass long seemed to be paying off.

The Greek team had left their stupid mascot behind.

Mrs Lincoln pleads with her husband not to go to that dangerous derby match but to come to the theatre instead.

A disputed penalty during the Xmas truce leads to an unseemly outbreak of violence in no-man's land.

In a vain attempt to find some pub called The Golden Fleece the lagernauts were doomed to miss the entire first half.

Viking raiders plunder coastal settlements in search of footballs.

David accuses Goliath of trying to get him sent off.

General Custer attempts to dribble to the corner flag to waste some time.

The Pompeii groundsman looks on in horror as the undersoil heating goes berserk.

It was Moses with his new fanzine.

No public transport for the Boxing Day fixture;
it was back to the bloody camels again.

The French FA move quickly to stamp out corruption.

Apache 2, Cheyenne 2. One more draw and Geronimo could give up living in a tent.

The big lad up front for the Tibetans was proving to be a bit of a handful.

The Black Death was playing havoc with team selection...

It was the runner from Marathon with the half-time scores.

Mr Shakespeare's impressive new football arena comes complete with sliding thatched roof.

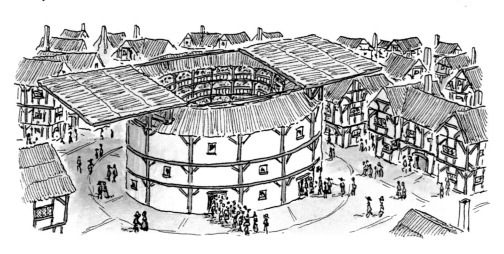

It was the dreaded gulag for linesmen who'd dared to flag Moscow Dynamo offside.

The inquisition relaxes in between persecutions with a bit of a kick around.

Egbert decided to have his contract extended rather than his height.

My new agent, Mr Machiavelli, takes a hard line in contract negotiations.

There wasn't much that could go wrong with a footballer that a bucket of leeches didn't seem to put right.

Accrington Agoraphobics are deducted another three points, failing to make the kick-off yet again.

These all-seater stadia were never going to catch on.

It was the lost tribe of the Amazon — and they wouldn't give the ball back.

The flat back four of the apocalypse were an intimidating sight.

The Arapaho pitch was enormous; the braves had disappeared upfield on the last attack days ago.

If Caesar said it was offside, then it was offside.

The Dutch purchase Manhattan island for two Ajax season tickets and a novelty hat.

The East India Company invests heavily in sponsorship and executive boxes.

Once again an eskimo cup tie is abandoned as another white ball disappears.

Yet another Yukon F. C. pitch invasion as gold is found in the kop end goalmouth.

A terrible away trip – set upon by hostile local fans. Where are the police when you need them?

Predictably, at the end of season dinner Jesus picked up the 'Player of the Year' award yet again.

Guy Fawkes decides against a pitch protest and elects to blow up the directors' box instead.

At half-time, Rony the Roman mascot entertained the crowd, fooling around with the Christian mascot.

The Canterbury fans' 'Becket Out'
campaign reaches a climax.

Puritans celebrate wildly as Cromwell makes it six.

Marco Polo demonstrated the offside trap he'd discovered in far-off Cathay.

Wyatt Earp dreaded these play-off shoot-outs.

It was the infamous ticket tout Jack the Rip-off.

Genghis Khan's half-time rollickings were legendary.

In Xanadu did Kublai Khan a 60,000 all-seater stadium decree...

Alfred the Great's matchday catering venture suffers technical problems.

Since the goalposts had been buried with the last chieftain, the tribe would have to make do with cloaks.

A transfer shock as Attila signs for Celtic.

Late for training again, Rasputin was ready for another spell in rehab.

A bored King Croesus decides to buy ... a football club.

Robin conceded that hiding in Sherwood Forest had its drawbacks on matchdays.

Vlad the Impaler headed for his third suspension of the season.

Large Roman squads made life difficult for the fourth officials.

Sooner or later they would have to ban the half-time smokes.

The U.S. cavalry had always been susceptible to nutmegs.

Elusive Houdini evades his markers once again.

The pre-match parachuting display had created problems for the groundstaff.

Maximus pondered over which chariot he should drive to training today.

Erik's fear of sailing ruled him out of European away games.

Ticketless Greek fans were still confident of getting in.

Novelty inflatables suffer an early setback in Germany.

The Apache medicine man gives up on Limping Bear's cruciate injury.

Curses, thought Shackleton, Smithers would be permanently offside now.

Keeper Pythagoras fails to get his angles right.

Mr Eiffel's new floodlights are impressive, but the club can't afford another three of those.

Young Elvis is disappointed to hear that his quiff was just not good enough for professional football.

Beau Geste attempts to conceal the Legion's injury crisis from the Riff.

It looked like Xerxes was employing his usual 50,000, 20,000, 30,000 formation.

Olaf had ruined the game yet again with his indiscipline.

U.S. Marines prepare for the first round of the Iwo Jima Cup.

Custer's scouts report the Sioux to be weak in attack and vulnerable at set pieces.

Disgruntled fans storm the winter palace of the club's decadent, wantaway centre forward.

The groundsman had never been the same since Nam.

Never mind hanging gardens, when were Babylon United going to put a roof on the toilets?

Scott's party wait in vain for Oates to bring the ball back.

Noah fails to fix the plumbing in the showers.

City's groundsman is found dead in mysterious circumstances.

Fugitive British airmen blow their cover to the Boche.

Disaster strikes as Whittle's patented 'Turbo-rattle' goes out of control.

Great relief in Mafeking as relegation is avoided.

The Mohican support had dwindled to almost nothing.

The rest of the knights knew nothing of his drink problem.

The referee insisted that Harold had to leave the field for treatment.

The team needed more height up front.

Tomkins had fallen foul of the local natives' primitive offside trap.

The Galapagos Cup Final is held up as one of the goalposts wanders off.

The new owners reassured everyone that the takeover would not change anything.

Seen from the reverse angle, it was clearly a penalty.

Mr Ford leaves early to manufacture some traffic.

Martin Luther nails up this week's team sheet — and the pope isn't on it!

Players compare executive bicycles.
Arkwrights had a chrome bell.

Robin Hood hands out over-priced season tickets to the peasantry.